INSIGHT  STUDIES

FROM SINNER TO SAINT

5 STUDIES ON HOLINESS FOR SMALL GROUPS AND INDIVIDUALS

BY JOHN CHAPMAN AND SIMON ROBERTS

From Sinner to Saint
© Matthias Media 2007

Matthias Media
(St Matthias Press Ltd ACN 067 558 365)
PO Box 225
Kingsford NSW 2032
Australia
Telephone: (02) 9663 1478; international: +61-2-9663-1478
Facsimile: (02) 9663 3265; international: +61-2-9663-3265
Email: info@matthiasmedia.com.au
Internet: www.matthiasmedia.com.au

Matthias Media (USA)
Telephone: 724 964 8152; international: +1-724-964-8152
Facsimile: 724 964 8166; international: +1-724-964-8166
Email: sales@matthiasmedia.com
Internet: www.matthiasmedia.com

Scripture quotations are from The Holy Bible, English Standard Version, copyright © 2001 by Crossway Bibles, a publishing ministry of Good News Publishers. Used by permission. All rights reserved.

ISBN 978 1 921068 84 3

All rights reserved. Except as may be permitted by the Copyright Act, no part of this publication may be reproduced in any form or by any means without prior permission from the publisher.

Cover design and overall series design by Lankshear Design Pty Ltd.
Typesetting by Matthias Media.

CONTENTS

Introduction to the studies 5

STUDY 1: God is holy—we are not 9

STUDY 2: How holiness is possible 17

STUDY 3: God's plan to make us holy 25

STUDY 4: Striving for holiness. 33

STUDY 5: The fulfilment of holiness 41

APPENDIX 1: Course overview 49

APPENDIX 2: Suggested timing for each study 53

INTRODUCTION TO THE STUDIES

How to make the most of these studies

While your Bible might come complete with a topical index, this certainly wasn't part of the original. In fact, the Bible was written by many different human authors over many hundreds of years. Yet because God is the ultimate author, the Bible makes sense as a whole and has much to say about a vast range of topics. This Bible study is designed to help you examine one of these topics: holiness.

Perhaps the best way to study this topic would be to read the Bible cover to cover and make your own topical index! Having discovered all the parts of the Bible which talk about this topic, you could then put all the pieces of the jigsaw together and summarize what the Bible as a whole says about holiness. However, most of us would benefit from a bit more guidance, and this is where this Bible study and the accompanying DVD can help.

This workbook will give you the road map for each study, including Bible passages to investigate and questions to think through. At various points you will be prompted to play a section of the accompanying DVD, where the Bible's teaching on holiness will be summarized and explained. Between your own investigation and discussion, and the teaching material presented on the DVD, we trust you will gain greater insight into this topic—seeing for yourself what the Bible has to say.

The format

Each study has up to four different types of material, each having its own symbol.

For starters: Questions to break the ice and get you thinking.

Investigate: Questions to help you investigate key parts of the Bible.

Look and listen: Video segments which summarize the Bible's teaching on a particular topic, integrating the Bible passages you have read and prompting you to think through the implications for yourself. It is a good idea to make notes during the video in the spaces provided in this workbook.

Think it through: Questions to help you think through the implications of your discoveries and write down your own thoughts and reactions.

Suggestions for individual study

Before you begin, pray that God would open your eyes to what he is saying in his word and give you the spiritual strength to do something about it. You may be spurred to pray again at the end of the study.

Work through the study, following the directions as you go. Write in the spaces provided.

Resist the temptation to skip over the **Think it through** sections. It is important to think about what is said in the video presentations (rather than just accepting them as true) and to ponder the implications for your life. Writing these things down is a very valuable way to get your thoughts working.

Take what opportunities you can to talk to others about what you've learnt.

Suggestions for group study

Much of the above applies to group study as well. The studies are suitable for structured Bible study or home groups, as well as for more informal pairs and threesomes. Each study is designed to take just under an hour to complete, although you may want to allow extra time if you want to discuss the material in more detail.

Everyone will get more out of the studies if each member of the group has done some preparation *beforehand*. In particular, people should work through the **For starters** and **Investigate** sections, making notes in the space provided. If people have worked through these sections then there should be plenty of time to watch the video material and discuss the **Think it through** questions.

Spend most of the group time discussing the **Investigate** *and* **Think it through** *sections.* If people have done some homework then you should be able to focus on what the passages mean, rather than on finding and reading them.

The role of the group leader is to direct the course of the discussion and to try to draw the threads together at the end. This will mean a little extra preparation—watching all the video sections for each study, working out which questions are worth concentrating on, and being sure of the main thrust of the study. To help group leaders understand the logic of the course and of each study, Appendix 1 on page 49 contains a course overview. Leaders will also probably want to work out approximately how long they want to spend on each part. See Appendix 2 for suggested timing for each study.

Check before the study commences that the DVD is properly loaded and cued to the right starting point. Make sure that everyone can see and hear the video presentations.

We haven't included an 'answers guide' to the questions in the studies. This is deliberate, for we want to give you a guided tour, not a lecture. However, there is more than enough information on the accompanying DVD to set you on the right path. The rest is up to you.

If you would like to do some further investigation into holiness, we highly recommend reading *A Sinner's Guide to Holiness* (see p. 58

for more details). It is also the ideal way for group leaders to do some extra preparation, since it provides further information and additional examples and case studies.

STUDY 1

GOD IS HOLY—
WE ARE NOT

For starters

What positive and negative images come to mind when you think of a 'holy' person?

Look and listen
Study 1: INTRODUCTION

Notes on video:

 **Investigate**

Read Job 38.

1. What struck you as you read this passage? How did you feel?

2. How far does God's power and control extend over the world? What is he able to do?

3. What words would you use to describe the God of Job 38?

Read Isaiah 6:1-7.

4. What does Isaiah see and hear?

5. What does Isaiah declare about himself?

6. What happens to Isaiah in verses 6-7? Why do you think this happens?

Look and listen
Study 1: HOLINESS AS POWER AND PURITY

Notes on video:

 **Investigate**

Read Jeremiah 8:4-9, 9:1-6.

1. Is human rebellion against God the exception or the rule? Why?

2. What kind of language is used to describe the way people (including God's people) have turned away from the Lord?

3. What accusations are brought against people in 9:1-6?

4. From these passages, what is God's verdict on human nature?

Look and listen
Study 1: WE ARE NOT LIKE GOD

Notes on video:

Think it through

1. What have you learnt from this study about who God is and what he is like?

2. What have you learnt about yourself?

3. What do you think is the biggest problem facing humanity?

STUDY 2
HOW HOLINESS IS POSSIBLE

Look and listen
Study 2: INTRODUCTION

Notes on video:

Investigate

(To save time, you might like to divide these verses between individuals, or groups of two or three, and have people report back to the group what they have discovered.)

1. What do the following verses tell us about Jesus?

   Luke 3:21-22

Luke 4:31-36

John 6:66-69

Acts 3:12-16

Hebrews 7:26-27

2. What do the following verses tell us about Jesus' mission?

Mark 10:45

John 3:16-17

Titus 2:11-14

3. What do the following verses tell us about how Jesus achieved his mission?

   Hebrews 10:11-14

   1 Peter 2:24

   1 Peter 3:18

   Titus 3:3-7

Look and listen
Study 2: CHRIST MAKES HOLINESS POSSIBLE

Notes on video:

# Investigate

Read Acts 26:12-20.

1. For what task did the Lord Jesus appoint Paul?

2. From this passage, how do people receive forgiveness for their sins?

3. From this passage, how are people sanctified (i.e. set apart and made holy)?

Read Colossians 1:21-23.

4. How does Paul describe what the Colossians once were?

5. What has now changed?

6. What must they continue to do?

Look and listen
Study 2: HOLINESS BEGINS WITH REPENTANCE AND FAITH

Notes on video:

 **Think it through**

1. Is holiness a gift from God or something we need to work at producing in our lives? Give reasons for your answer.

2. What is the place of repentance in everyday Christian life?

3. What has challenged you from this study? What has provided comfort and encouragement?

STUDY 3

GOD'S PLAN TO MAKE US HOLY

For starters

Whom do you most admire? Why?

Look and listen
Study 3: INTRODUCTION

Notes on video:

 **Investigate**

Read Romans 8:28-30.

1. What is God's purpose for those who love him?

2. What do you think it means to "be conformed to the image of his Son" (v. 29)?

Read Titus 2:11-14.

3. What titles and descriptions are used of Jesus in this passage?

4. What kind of life does Jesus rescue us *from*?

5. What kind of life does Jesus rescue us *for*?

# Look and listen
Study 3: GOD'S PLAN IS TO MAKE US LIKE CHRIST—HOLY AND BLAMELESS

Notes on video:

 **Investigate**

(To save time, you might like to divide these verses between individuals, or groups of two or three, and have people report back to the group what they have discovered.)

Read 1 Thessalonians 4:1-3, 5:19-24 and Philippians 2:12-13.

1. How are Christians to proceed and progress in their faith?

2. Who is responsible for our progression in holiness?

3. How does this teaching challenge you? How does it reassure you?

FROM SINNER TO SAINT

Look and listen
Study 3: HOLINESS PROGRESSES THE WAY IT BEGAN— BY REPENTANCE AND FAITH

Notes on video:

# Think it through

1. God's plan is to make his people like Christ. How can you spend more time reflecting on the teaching and example of the Lord Jesus?

2. What practical steps can you take to learn more about Jesus Christ?

3. In what areas do you struggle to be holy—to be like Christ?

4. If holiness progresses by repentance and faith, what are some of the dangers and distractions that prevent you from making progress in holiness?

STUDY 4

STRIVING FOR HOLINESS

 **For starters**

"If you want to be holy, you need to 'let go and let God'. If you really trust him with all your heart, then God will make you holy." Do you agree or disagree with this statement? Why?

Look and listen
Study 4: INTRODUCTION

Notes on video:

Investigate

Read Hebrews 12:1-17.

1. What is the prize we are striving for?

2. How should we run the race God has set before us?

3. This passage exhorts us to look to Jesus, "the founder and perfecter of our faith" (v. 2). What do we learn about our Lord's life in these verses? What do we learn from his example?

4. Why is God the Father's discipline such a good thing? What does it produce?

5. What sorts of things can distract us from this race?

Look and listen
Study 4: SELF-DISCIPLINE AND GOD'S DISCIPLINE

Notes on video:

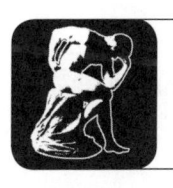

Think it through

Read 1 John 1:8-2:6.

1. Two responses to sin are given in this passage: denial and confession. What are the consequences of each?

2. John doesn't want Christians to sin. That's why he wrote this letter. Do you think it's possible for a Christian to be entirely free of sin? Why/why not?

3. What help and comfort is available to the person who sins?

Read Luke 22:39-46.

4. Was it easy for Jesus to resist temptation and be obedient?

5. What does Jesus do in his hour of temptation? What does he tell his disciples to do so that they may not "enter into temptation"?

Look and listen
Study 4: THERE IS NO SUCH THING AS INSTANT AND EFFORTLESS HOLINESS

Notes on video:

Think it through

1. We all face trials and temptations. What are some common difficulties that hinder the Christian walk? What have you learnt from this study about how to undergo trials and withstand temptations?

2. How do you think Christians should deal with failure in this area?

STUDY 5

THE FULFILMENT OF HOLINESS

For starters

How often would you say you thought about eternity (i.e. life in God's new creation)?

Look and listen
Study 5: INTRODUCTION

Notes on video:

Investigate

Read 2 Peter 3:8-13.

1. What do we learn about "the day of the Lord"?

2. How does the coming "day of the Lord" affect the here and now?

Read Revelation 21:1-8, 22-27.

3. How are the new heavens and the new earth described?

4. What will have no place in this new age?

5. How is the reality described in this passage an incentive to strive for holiness?

Look and listen
Study 5: THE FULFILMENT OF HOLINESS

Notes on video:

Investigate

1. From the following passages, what things get in the way of people following Jesus to the end?

    James 4:1-10

    Luke 8:11-15

Read Hebrews 3:12-19.

2. What danger does this passage warn us about?

3. How do we avoid this danger?

Look and listen
Study 5: THE DANGER OF DISTRACTION

Notes on video:

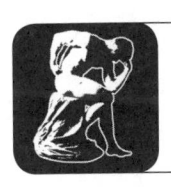

Think it through

1. What are some practical steps we can take to make sure we are not distracted from the hope we have?

2. How can we encourage one another to persevere in holiness?

3. Think back over the last five studies. What is the most significant thing you have learnt? What is the biggest challenge you face as a result?

APPENDIX 1

COURSE OVERVIEW

From Sinner to Saint is a series of five studies on the topic of holiness. The 'Introduction to the studies' on page 5 of this workbook tells you more about the studies and how to use them. This overview section is designed to explain briefly the logical connections between the five studies so that the study leader has a better understanding of the flow of the course.

Study 1: God is holy—we are not

To understand holiness, we first need to understand God: he is the holy one, the one who is powerful and pure. In this respect, God is quite unlike us. God is in control of all things, and has the power to do whatever he wishes. By a simple word he created all things, and likewise he controls and upholds his world. Not only is God powerful, he is pure: his use of power is always for good.

This picture of God stands in stark contrast to human nature and behaviour. Our power and control over the world is very limited, and what power we have we invariably use for evil. The result is that we are alienated from God and unable to stand in his presence. In the Bible, whenever people are confronted by God's holiness, their first reaction is to draw back, fearfully recognizing that they are unworthy and unable to stand before God. This is the starting point for our study of holiness: God is holy. We are not. Having acknowledged this, we can begin to explore what the gospel has to say about how holiness is possible.

Study 2: How holiness is possible

Holiness is only possible because of Jesus. Jesus was different from the rest of humanity in one important respect: he was holy like his Father. The good news for humanity is that the Lord Jesus' mission was to save people from the judgement we deserve as sinners, and draw to himself a people who are devoted to holiness. Significantly, Jesus achieved his mission as the Christ by dying on a cross. Our holiness is only possible because of Jesus' death on our behalf, and the washing of regeneration and renewal by the Holy Spirit. The Christian turns away from wrongdoing and looks to Jesus to provide him with a new status before God as one of his holy children, and then begins a new life devoted to what is good, not evil.

Study 3: God's plan to make us holy

Even though because of Christ we have the status of God's holy people, we still need to put away sin and put on good works in our daily lives. Study 3 explores God's plan to make us holy—in other words, to make us like Christ. The Lord Jesus has rescued us *from* sin and condemnation, *for* godliness and good works. In undertaking this task, we have not been left to our own resources; the God who has rescued us is presently working by his word and Spirit to transform us into the image of his son. In this work, God does not bypass our minds and wills, nor does he instantly change us. God has woken and regenerated our inner beings so that we can understand what is good and choose to do what is good. We must do the hard work of putting off old sinful habits and putting on good works.

Study 4: Striving for holiness

Study 4 continues where Study 3 left off. We have a role to play in cultivating holiness in our lives. We need to strive for holiness. It will take effort, discipline and endurance. The Lord Jesus Christ is a great role model who exemplifies these characteristics, so we ought to look to him not only as the one who provides salvation, but as the one who has 'been there and done that'. In the face of intense temptation and persecution, Jesus always resisted sin and did the right thing. In our own lives, we ought to display the same stubborn determination to be holy before our heavenly Father.

However, there is no such thing as instant and effortless holiness. We are like those who are recovering from an illness: the core disease of sin and judgement has been dealt with, but we are still weak and plagued by symptoms. But in Jesus we have an advocate with the Father. God is faithful, and he will forgive us our sins if we abide in him.

Study 5: The fulfilment of holiness

Study 5 examines the fulfilment of holiness. Our struggle to be holy has an end. On the last day God will do away with evil and establish his new creation where righteousness will dwell. The judgement and new creation are an incentive for holy living now because we know that there is no future in sin, only in holiness. The judgement and new creation are a comfort, for we know that on that last day God will fully and finally transform us into the holy people he wants us to be. In the meantime, we must not be distracted from the hope we have; rather, we ought to encourage one another to persevere in holiness. By continually returning to and exploring the message of the gospel of our Lord Jesus Christ, we can remain focused on the race set before us.

APPENDIX 2
SUGGESTED TIMING FOR EACH STUDY

Not all questions are created equal! Particularly with a topical study such as this one, some questions are designed to help you note a simple point that a passage makes, while other questions will take longer to talk over properly.

Remember, the aim of these studies is to gain a better understanding of holiness, and not to look at every passage in such fine detail that every last ounce of meaning is extracted. Each passage *should* be taken in context and correctly understood, but the focus is on putting all the pieces of the holiness 'jigsaw' together. So you should leave plenty of time for discussion. It won't help the group if you spend all your time on the **Investigate** sections without leaving enough time for the **Think it through** sections.

To help group leaders estimate how long to spend on each section of the studies, we have included the following 'run-sheets'. These assume that each study takes one hour, so if your group meets for longer, you will need to modify the timings accordingly. To do the study in an hour, each member should have already looked up each passage and made notes in their workbook. You should also make sure you have the DVD loaded and ready to start at the introduction section for that study.

Study 1: God is holy—we are not

Section	Suggested Timing	Your Timing
For starters	3	
Look and listen: Introduction	2	2
Investigate	20	
Look and listen: Holiness as power and purity	6	6
Investigate	15	
Look and listen: We are not like God	4	4
Think it through	10	
TOTAL	60 min	

Study 2: How holiness is possible

Section	Suggested Timing	Your Timing
Look and listen: Introduction	1	1
Investigate	22	
Look and listen: Christ makes holiness possible	3	3
Investigate	15	
Look and listen: Holiness begins with repentance and faith	4	4
Think it through	15	
TOTAL	60 min	

Study 3: God's plan to make us holy

Section	Suggested Timing	Your Timing
For starters	3	
Look and listen: Introduction	1	1
Investigate	15	
Look and listen: God's plan is to make us like Christ—holy and blameless	5	5
Investigate	20	
Look and listen: Holiness progresses the way it began—by repentance and faith	4	4
Think it through	12	
TOTAL	60 min	

Study 4: Striving for holiness

Section	Suggested Timing	Your Timing
For starters	4	
Look and listen: Introduction	2	2
Investigate	12	
Look and listen: Self-discipline and God's discipline	5	5
Think it through	18	
Look and listen: There is no such thing as instant and effortless holiness	4	4
Think it through	15	
TOTAL	60 min	

Study 5: The fulfilment of holiness

Section	Suggested Timing	Your Timing
For starters	4	
Look and listen: Introduction	2	2
Investigate	15	
Look and listen: The fulfilment of holiness	4	4
Investigate	15	
Look and listen: The danger of distraction	5	5
Think it through	15	
TOTAL	60 min	

matthiasmedia

Matthias Media is a ministry team of like-minded, evangelical Christians working together to achieve a particular goal, as summarized in our mission statement:

To serve our Lord Jesus Christ, and the growth of his gospel in the world, by producing and delivering high quality, Bible-based resources.

It was in 1988 that we first started pursuing this mission together, and in God's kindness we now have more than 250 different ministry resources being distributed all over the world. These resources range from Bible studies and books, through to training courses and audio sermons.

To find out more about our large range of very useful products, and to access samples and free downloads, visit our website:

www.matthiasmedia.com.au

How to buy our resources

1. Direct from us over the internet:
   - in the US: www.matthiasmedia.com
   - in Australia and the rest of the world: www.matthiasmedia.com.au

2. Direct from us by phone:
   - in the US: 1 866 407 4530
   - in Australia: 1800 814 360 (Sydney: 9663 1478)
   - international: +61-2-9663-1478

3. Through a range of outlets in various parts of the world. Visit **www.matthiasmedia.com.au/international.php** for details about recommended retailers in your part of the world, including www.thegoodbook.co.uk in the United Kingdom.

4. Trade enquiries can be addressed to:
   - in the US: sales@matthiasmedia.com
   - in the UK: sales@ivpbooks.com
   - in Australia and the rest of the world: sales@matthiasmedia.com.au

GUIDEBOOKS FOR LIFE

A Sinner's Guide to Holiness
By John Chapman

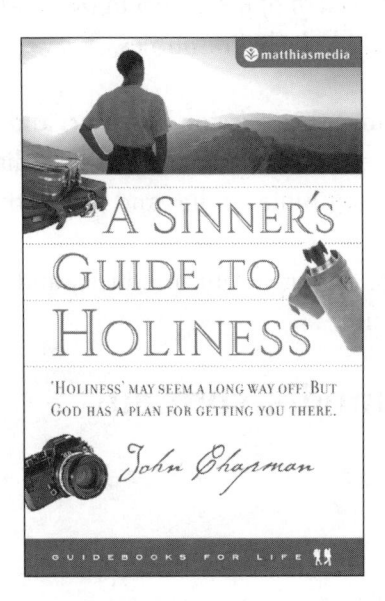

What is holiness? Why do I need it? And why is it such a struggle for me to achieve holiness in my everyday life?

In *A Sinner's Guide to Holiness*, well-known evangelist John Chapman explores the nuts and bolts of what the Bible has to say about holiness—where it begins, how it makes progress in our lives, and its ultimate fulfilment as we are changed into Christ's glorious likeness on the Last Day.

This is a timely publication in this day and age, when we often lose sight of the holiness of God.

A Sinner's Guide to Holiness is part of Matthias Media's Guidebooks for Life series. This series aims to dig into the Bible and discover what God is telling us there, and then apply that truth to our daily Christian lives. It covers important topics and issues of the Christian life—such as prayer, guidance, and holiness. For up-to-date information on the latest in this series, visit our website.

FOR MORE INFORMATION OR TO ORDER CONTACT:

Matthias Media
Telephone: +61-2-9663-1478
Facsimile: +61-2-9663-3265
Email: sales@matthiasmedia.com.au
www.matthiasmedia.com.au

Matthias Media (USA)
Ph: 1-866-407-4530
Fax: 724-964-8166
Email: sales@matthiasmedia.com
www.matthiasmedia.com

INSIGHT STUDIES

Where to Lord?
6 studies on guidance for small groups and individuals

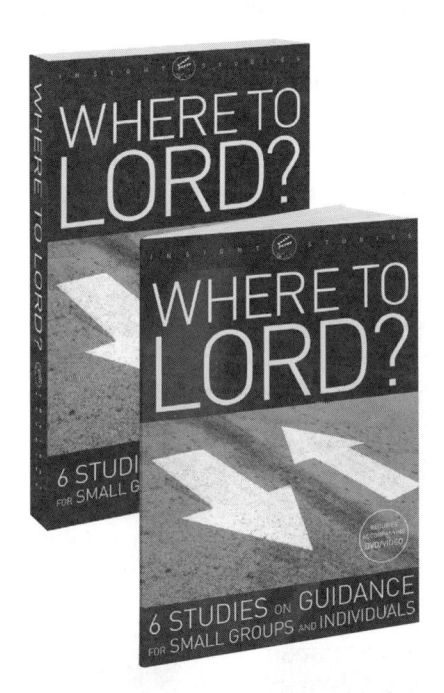

Guidance can be one of the most frustrating issues for Christians. We know that Jesus has died, and that heaven lies in the future. But we remain unsure about everything in between. We have many questions about guidance, such as:

- How does God guide his people today?
- What does God want me to do with my life?
- Where does he want me to work?
- Who does he want me to marry?
- How can I know God's will for my life?
- Am I missing out on God's personal guidance?
- How do I hear his voice?

These six studies on guidance will help you plot a course through these difficult issues.

Where to, Lord is part of our Insight Studies series, which uses a mix of Bible investigation, group discussion and video input to help you interact with God's word. Perfect for groups looking for a refreshing change, the studies and DVD format are specifically designed to work together to enable any group to put together the pieces on difficult topics such as guidance and holiness.

FOR MORE INFORMATION OR TO ORDER CONTACT:

Matthias Media
Telephone: +61-2-9663-1478
Facsimile: +61-2-9663-3265
Email: sales@matthiasmedia.com.au
www.matthiasmedia.com.au

Matthias Media (USA)
Ph: 1-866-407-4530
Fax: 724-964-8166
Email: sales@matthiasmedia.com
www.matthiasmedia.com

PATHWAY BIBLE GUIDES

Pathway Bible Guides

Pathway Bible Guides are simple, straightforward easy-to-read Bible studies, ideal for groups who are new to studying the Bible, or groups with limited time for study.

We've designed the studies to be short and easy to use, with an uncomplicated vocabulary. At the same time, we've tried to do justice to the passages being studied, and to model good Bible-reading principles. Pathway Bible Guides are simple without being simplistic; no-nonsense without being no-content.

Beginning with God
Genesis 1-12

Getting to Know God
Exodus 1-20

The Art of Living
Proverbs

Seeing Things God's Way
Daniel

Following Jesus
Luke 9-12

Peace with God
Romans

Church Matters
1 Corinthians 1-7

Standing Firm
1 Thessalonians

FOR MORE INFORMATION OR TO ORDER CONTACT:

Matthias Media
Telephone: +61-2-9663-1478
Facsimile: +61-2-9663-3265
Email: sales@matthiasmedia.com.au
www.matthiasmedia.com.au

Matthias Media (USA)
Ph: 1-866-407-4530
Fax: 724-964-8166
Email: sales@matthiasmedia.com
www.matthiasmedia.com